Look and Find

Bunny Rabbit

and Her Friends

Phineas Frogg • Dorothy Duck

Henrietta Hen • Katie Kittie

Roxie Raccoon • And more!

Illustrated by Bob Terrio

Cover illustrated by Bob Terrio and Jerry Tiritilli

Illustration Assistant: Gale Terrio

Illustration script development by Jane Jerrard

Louis Weber, C.E.O.
Publications International, Ltd.
7373 North Cicero Avenue
Lincolnwood, Illinois 60646

Permission is never granted for commercial purposes.

Manufactured in the U.S.A.

8 7 6 5 4 3 2 1

ISBN 1-56173-530-2

PUBLICATIONS INTERNATIONAL, LTD.

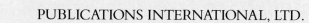

Bunny is a good little rabbit—*nearly* all the time. But today she's up to a bit of mischief in Farmer Brown's garden!

Find Bunny Rabbit. Then look for her partners in crime!

Bunny Rabbit

Lucie Goose

Sammy Skunk

Sherlock Tortoise

Francis Bacon

Phineas Frogg

Roxie Raccoon

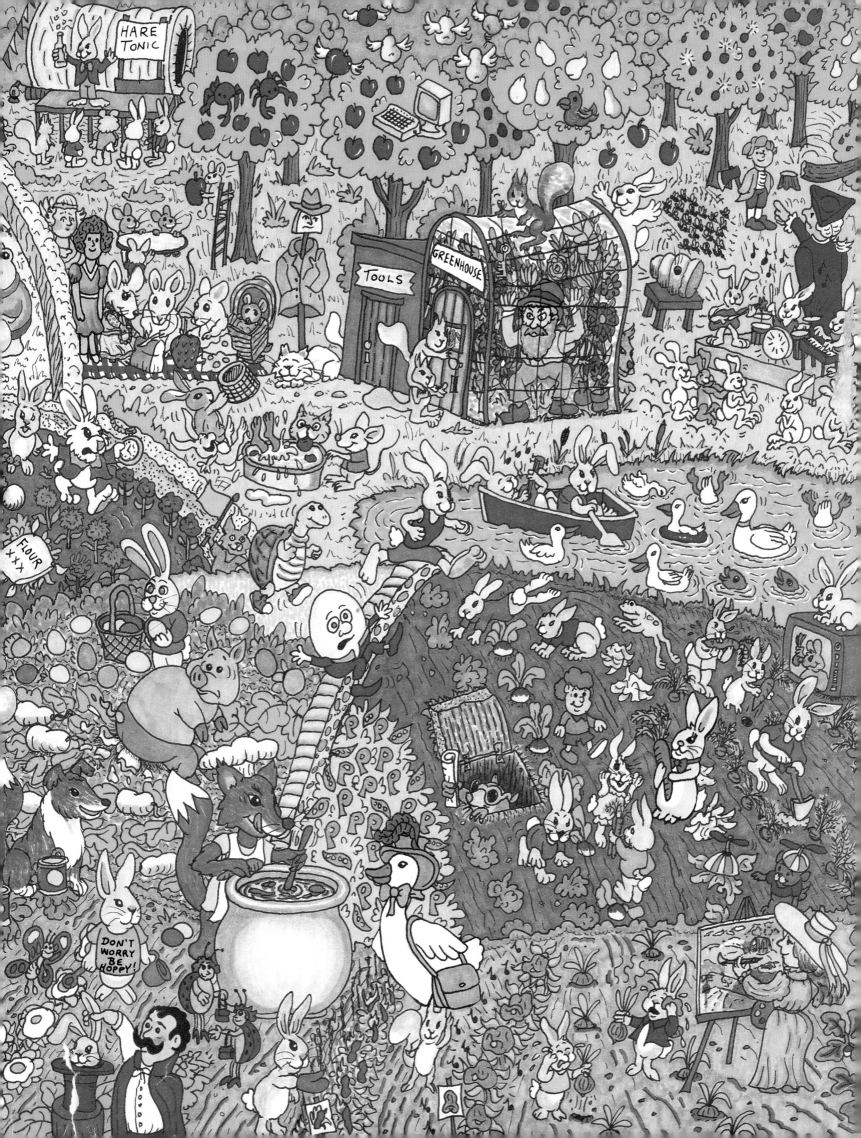

One rainy day, Bunny Rabbit decided to play with her dollhouse. There was a surprise waiting for her dolls, though. A mouse family had moved in!

Can you find these things the mice are using in their new home? Can you find Bunny Rabbit hiding, too?

Bunny Rabbit

A postage stamp

A bottle cap

A chess piece

A domino

A toothbrush

A thimble

A crayon

Things are so peaceful and quiet on Farmer Brown's farm. Or are they? Bunny Rabbit thinks she can sneak into the cabbage patch unnoticed!

Find Bunny Rabbit. Then look for these farm animals and farm things.

Bunny Rabbit

Lucie Goose

A collie dog

Dorothy Duck

A pig "pen"

A "horse shoe"

A cow "belle"

"Kid" gloves

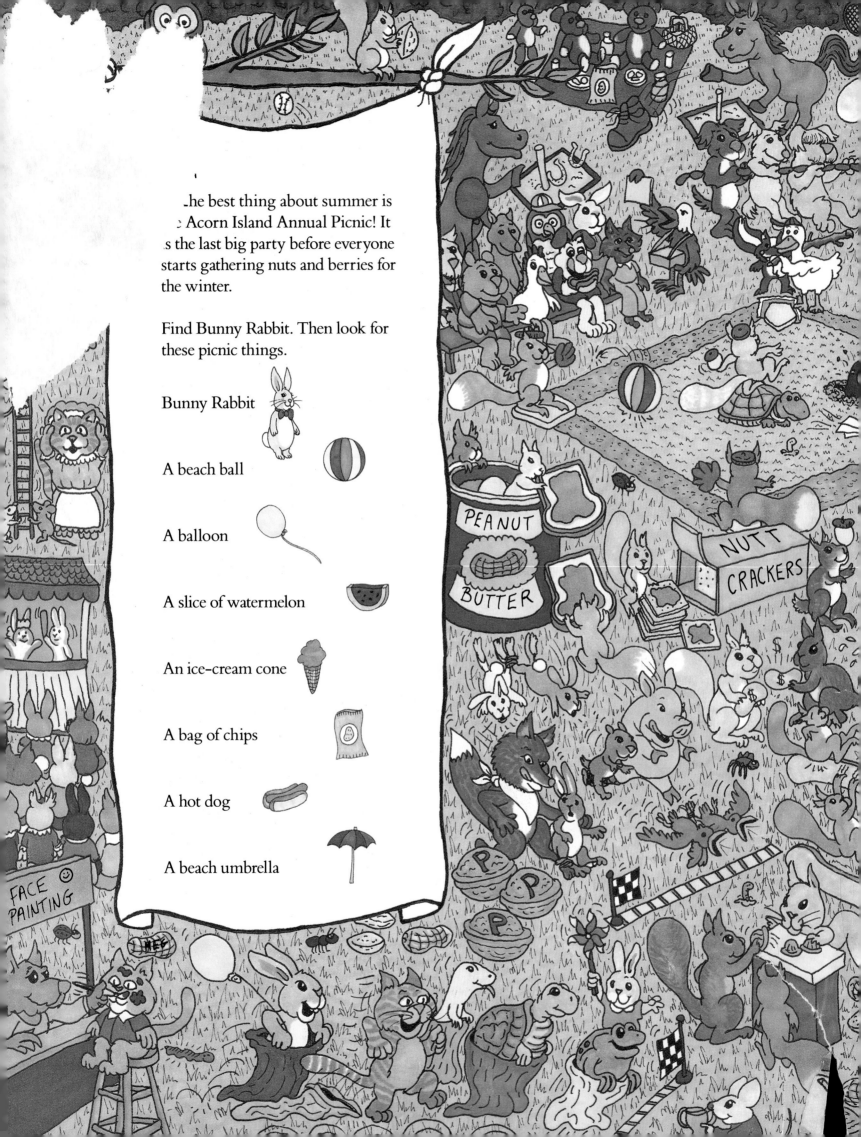

The best thing about summer is the Acorn Island Annual Picnic! It is the last big party before everyone starts gathering nuts and berries for the winter.

Find Bunny Rabbit. Then look for these picnic things.

Bunny Rabbit

A beach ball

A balloon

A slice of watermelon

An ice-cream cone

A bag of chips

A hot dog

A beach umbrella

DOWN WITH EGG TOSSING

NO EGG TOSS

Mr. Brown

TO NUTHOUSE

Bunny Rabbit is having a surprise birthday party for Sammy Skunk! But where is he? Will he miss his own party?

Can you find Sammy Skunk? Can you find these "nosy" friends who are trying to sniff him out?

Sammy Skunk

Bunny Rabbit

Betty Bloodhound

Arnold Anteater

Edith Elephant

Toulouse Toucan

Ricky Rhino

Sylvia Swordfish

HAPPY BIRTHDAY SAMM

The Country Store is having a big sale! Bunny Rabbit has found a good bargain on garden tools. Lucie Goose is hoping to buy a new bonnet.

After you find Bunny Rabbit, look for these other customers who have come from farm and field for this once-a-year event.

Bunny Rabbit

Lucie Goose

Sammy Skunk

Katie Kittie

Petunia Pigg

Henrietta Hen

Phineas Frogg

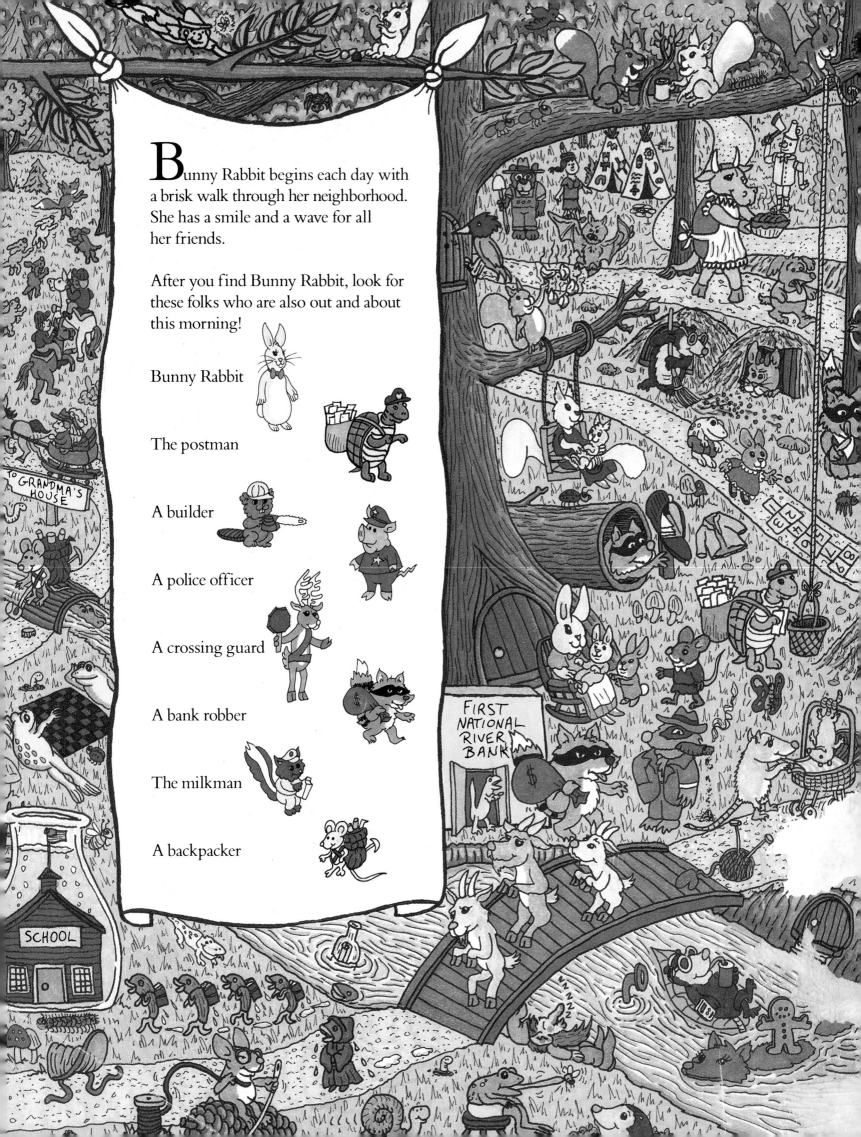

Bunny Rabbit begins each day with a brisk walk through her neighborhood. She has a smile and a wave for all her friends.

After you find Bunny Rabbit, look for these folks who are also out and about this morning!

Bunny Rabbit

The postman

A builder

A police officer

A crossing guard

A bank robber

The milkman

A backpacker

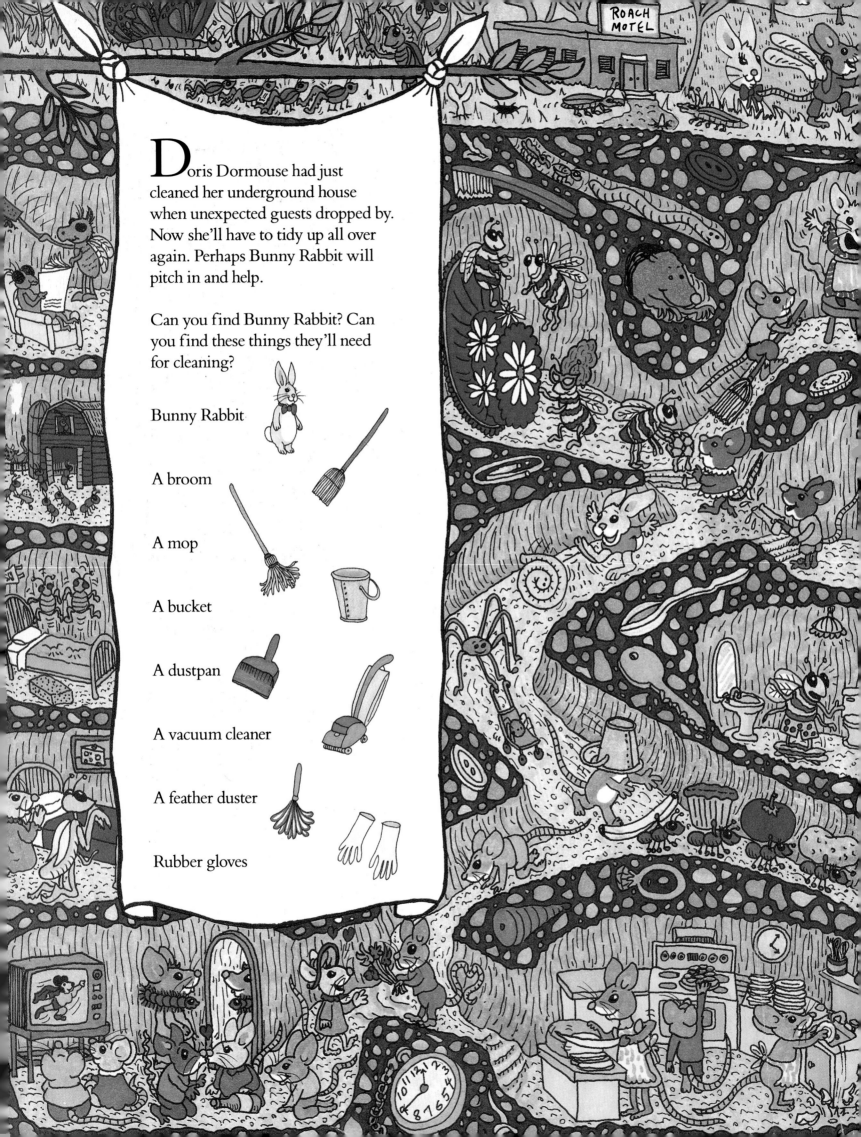

ROACH MOTEL

Doris Dormouse had just cleaned her underground house when unexpected guests dropped by. Now she'll have to tidy up all over again. Perhaps Bunny Rabbit will pitch in and help.

Can you find Bunny Rabbit? Can you find these things they'll need for cleaning?

Bunny Rabbit

A broom

A mop

A bucket

A dustpan

A vacuum cleaner

A feather duster

Rubber gloves

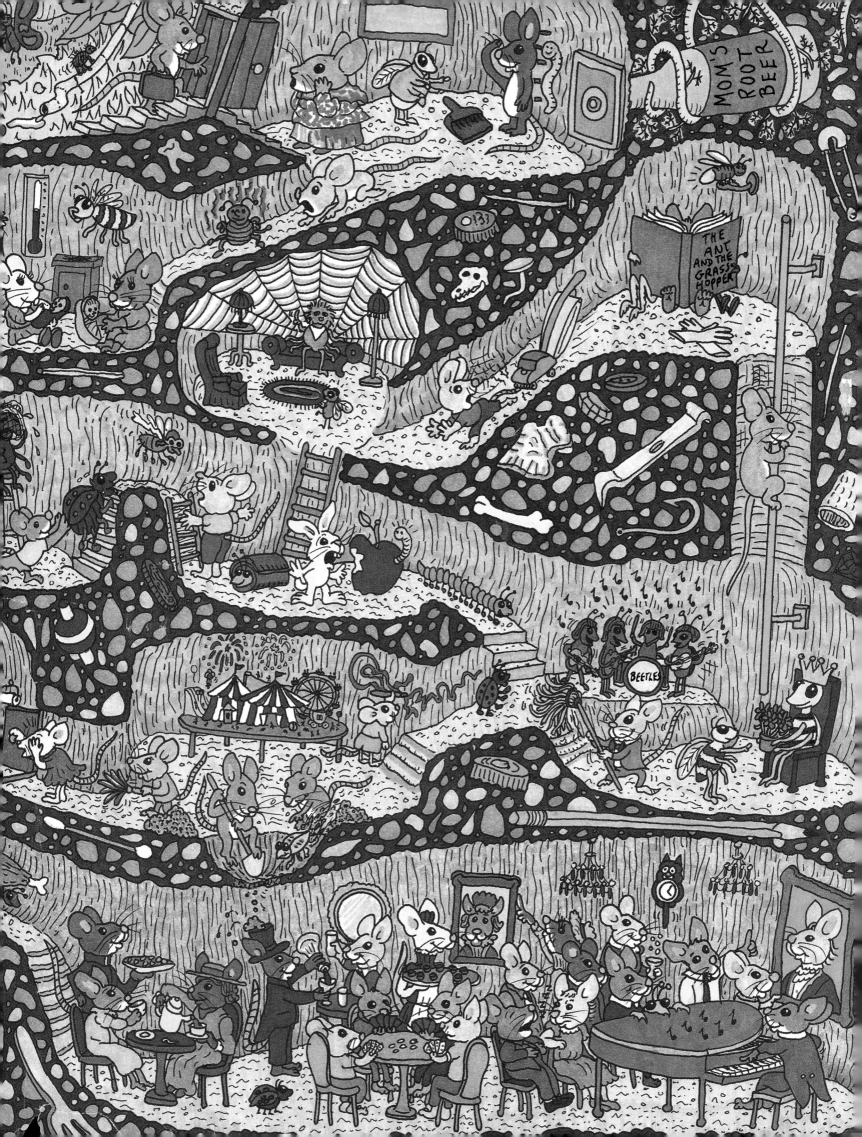

It's bedtime at Bunny Rabbit's house. Mama Rabbit would like a little peace and quiet, but her children have different plans.

Have fun finding Bunny Rabbit and her naughty brothers and sisters!

Bunny Rabbit

Billy Rabbit

Betty Rabbit

Bucky Rabbit

Bonny Rabbit

Benny Rabbit

Buffy Rabbit

Becky Rabbit

Take another stroll in Bunny Rabbit's woods. Can you find these funny things?

- ☐ A school of fish
- ☐ A bald eagle
- ☐ Little Red Riding Hood
- ☐ Three Billy Goats Gruff
- ☐ Peter Pan
- ☐ A cow pie
- ☐ A church mouse
- ☐ Mr. Toad's Wild Ride

The naughty mouse children never put away their things. Can you find these toys in the messy dollhouse?

- ☐ A teddy bear
- ☐ A red wagon
- ☐ A spinning top
- ☐ A beach ball
- ☐ A tricycle
- ☐ Roller skates
- ☐ A ballerina doll
- ☐ A dump truck
- ☐ A robot

Go back to the not-so-sleepy little Rabbits' house to find these bedtime things.

- ☐ A toothbrush
- ☐ A teddy bear
- ☐ A book of bedtime stories
- ☐ An alarm clock
- ☐ A hot-water bottle
- ☐ A cradle
- ☐ A pair of bunny slippers
- ☐ A glass of milk

Did Doris Dormouse's house drive you buggy? Go back to look for these creepy-crawlies!

- ☐ A flea circus
- ☐ A queen bee
- ☐ A beehive hairdo
- ☐ A daddy longlegs
- ☐ The Itsy Bitsy Spider
- ☐ A yellow jacket
- ☐ A stinkbug
- ☐ An ant farm
- ☐ The "Beetles" rock band